Bob and Eddie
in the Kitchen

Cathy Gale

Little Hippo

"Let's make a cake!" says Bob.
"Open the cookery book, please Eddie."

"We need flour and sugar," says Bob.
"Get them from the cupboard,
   please Eddie."

"We need butter and eggs," says Bob.
"Look in the fridge, please Eddie."

"Mix it all together," says Bob.
"Put it in the oven, please Eddie."

"I can't wait for the cake," says Bob.

"Let's have toast! Open the jam, please Eddie."

"I can smell burning," says Bob.
"Catch the toast, please Eddie!"

"Time to ice the cake," says Bob.
"Open the icing sugar, please Eddie."

"That was brilliant cake, Bob!" says Eddie.
"Can we make another one soon please?"